★SHOWSTOPPERS
AUDITION SONGS

WISE PUBLICATIONS
PART OF THE MUSIC SALES GROUP
LONDON / NEW YORK / PARIS / SYDNEY / COPENHAGEN / BERLIN / MADRID / HONG KONG / TOKYO

Published by
WISE PUBLICATIONS
14-15 Berners Street, London W1T 3LJ, UK.

Exclusive Distributors:
MUSIC SALES LIMITED
Distribution Centre, Newmarket Road,
Bury St Edmunds, Suffolk IP33 3YB, UK.
MUSIC SALES PTY LIMITED
20 Resolution Drive,
Caringbah, NSW 2229, Australia.

Order No. AM995940
ISBN 978-1-84772-816-6
This book © Copyright 2010 Wise Publications,
a division of Music Sales Limited.

Music edited by Jenni Wheeler
Printed in the EU

CD recorded, mixed and mastered by Jonas Persson
Backing tracks arranged by Paul Honey
Guitars by Arthur Dick

Your Guarantee of Quality:
As publishers, we strive to produce every book
to the highest commercial standards.
The music has been freshly engraved and the book has
been carefully designed to minimise awkward page turns
and to make playing from it a real pleasure.
Particular care has been given to specifying acid-free,
neutral-sized paper made from pulps which have not been
elemental chlorine bleached.
This pulp is from farmed sustainable forests and was
produced with special regard for the environment.
Throughout, the printing and binding have been planned
to ensure a sturdy, attractive publication which should give
years of enjoyment.
If your copy fails to meet our high standards, please
inform us and we will gladly replace it.

www.musicsales.com

AND I AM TELLING YOU I'M NOT GOING

WORDS BY TOM EYEN
MUSIC BY HENRY KRIEGER

9

BE ITALIAN

WORDS & MUSIC BY MAURY YESTON

-gi - na will tell you: if you want to make a wom - an hap - py,

you re - ly on what you were born with, be-cause it is in your blood.

molto rit.

Più mosso (♩ = 70)

1. Be I - tal - ian, be I - tal - ian, take a
(2.) gen - tle, sen - ti - men - tal, go a -

15

chance and try to steal a fier - y kiss.
- head and try to give my cheek a pat.

Be I-
But be

-tal - ian,_____ be I - tal - ian,
dar - ing,_____ and un - car - ing,

when you
when you

1.

hold me, don't just hold me, but hold this!
pinch me, try to

Ha, ha, ha, ha, ha, ha.

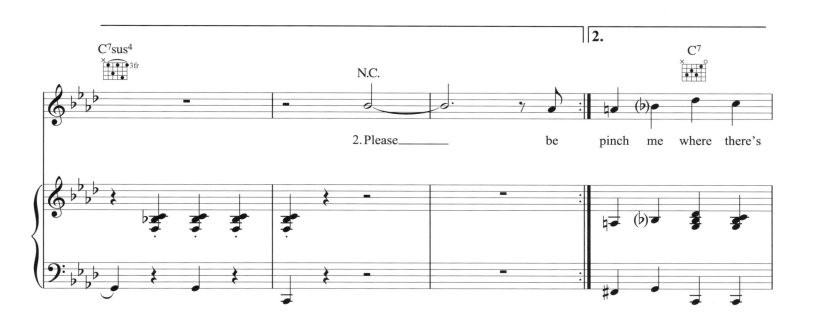

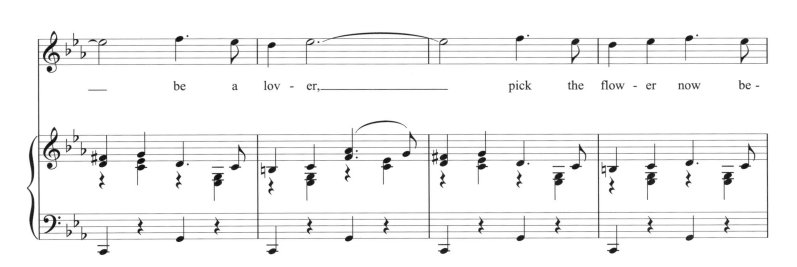

be a lov - er,＿＿＿＿＿＿＿＿ pick the flow - er now be -

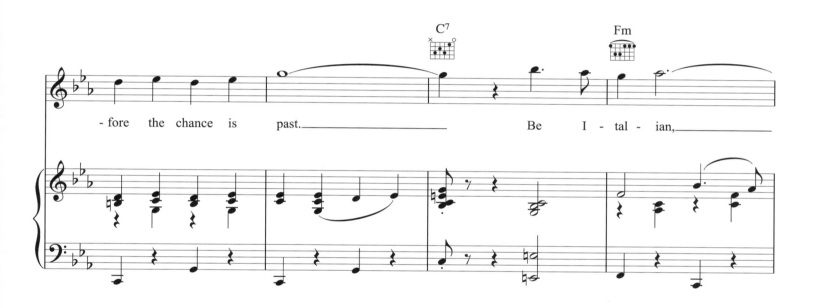

- fore the chance is past.＿＿＿＿＿＿＿ Be I - tal - ian,＿＿＿＿＿＿

— be I - tal - ian, live to - day as if it

DEFYING GRAVITY

WORDS & MUSIC BY STEPHEN SCHWARTZ

GOOD MORNING BALTIMORE

WORDS & MUSIC BY MARC SHAIMAN & SCOTT WITTMAN

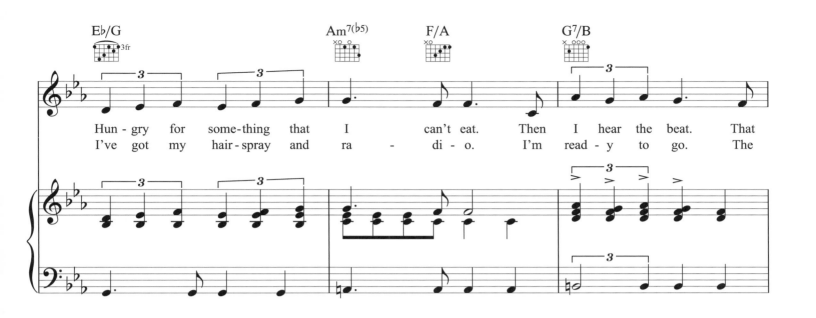

Hun - gry for some-thing that I can't eat. Then I hear the beat. That
I've got my hair-spray and ra - di - o. I'm read - y to go. The

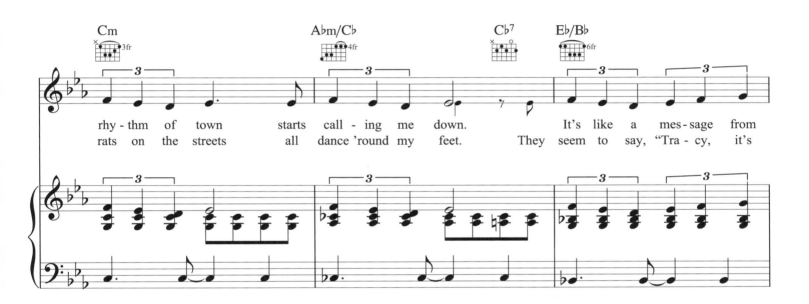

rhy - thm of town starts call - ing me down. It's like a mes - sage from
rats on the streets all dance 'round my feet. They seem to say, "Tra - cy, it's

high a - bove____ Oh, oh, oh. Pull - ing me out to the
up to you."_____ So, oh, oh. Don't hold me back, 'cause to -

smiles and the streets that I love. Good morn - ing, Bal - ti - more!
-day all my dreams will come true. Good morn - ing, Bal - ti - more!

Ev - 'ry day's like an o - pen door.
There's the flash - er who lives next door.

Ev - 'ry night is a
There's the bum on his

fan - ta - sy.
bar - room stool.

Ev - 'ry sound's like a sym - pho - ny.
They wish me luck on my way to school.

Good morn - ing, Bal - ti - more! And some day when I

take to the floor, the world's gon-na wake up and __ see

1.

Bal - ti - more and me.

27

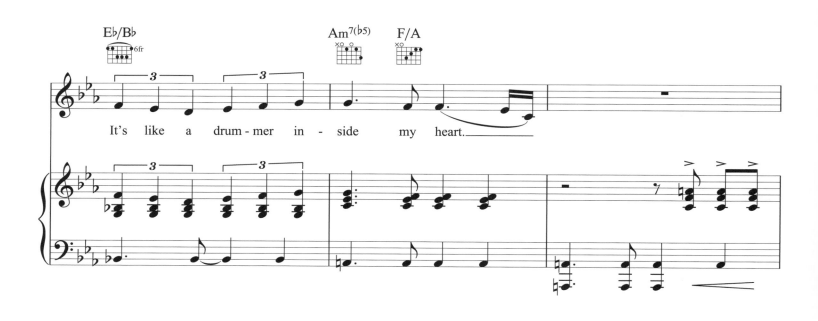

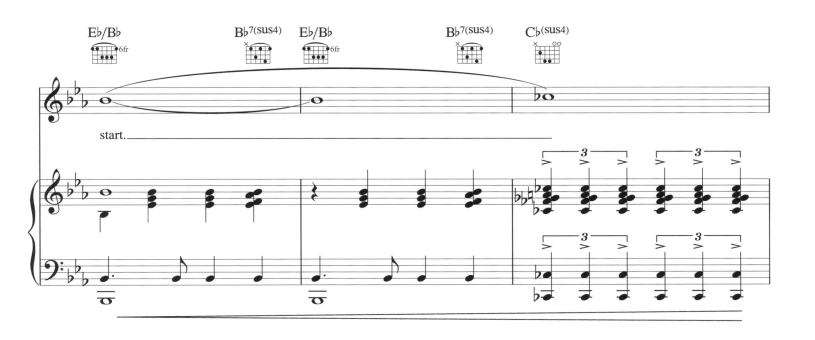

I love you, Bal - ti - more! Ev - 'ry day's like an

o - pen____ door.____ Ev - 'ry night is a fan - ta - sy.

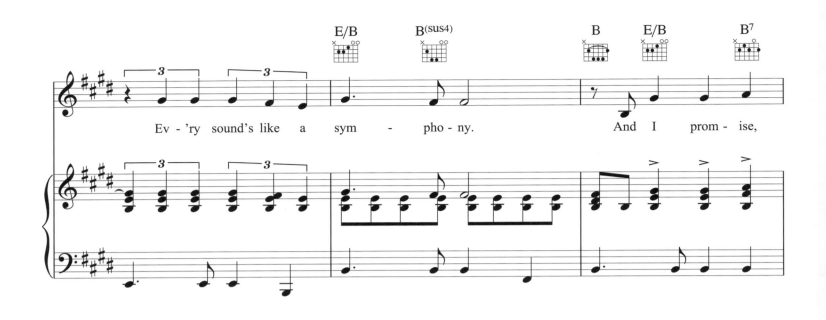

Ev - 'ry sound's like a sym - pho - ny. And I prom - ise,

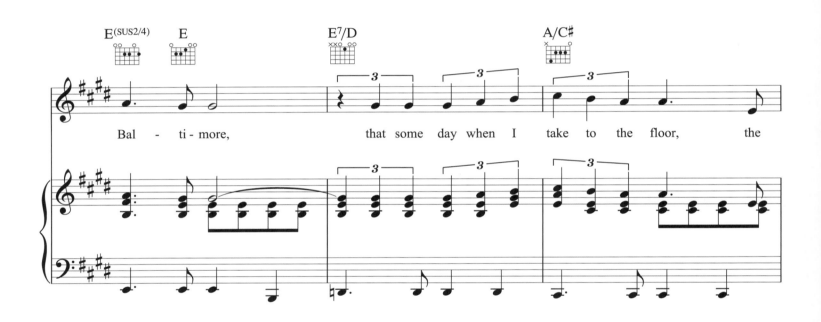

Bal - ti - more, that some day when I take to the floor, the

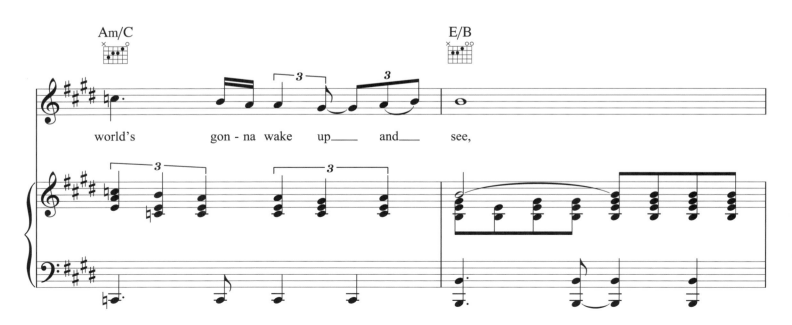

world's gon - na wake up___ and___ see,

gon - na wake up and see_____ Bal - ti - more and

me. Bal - ti - more__ and__ me,

Bal - ti - more and____ me!_____

MAMA WHO BORE ME

WORDS BY STEVEN SATER
MUSIC BY DUNCAN SHEIK

And some_ just lie_ there, cry - ing for Him to come_ and find_ them. But when He comes,_ they don't_ know how to go._

Ma - ma,_ who bore_ me,

Ma - ma,_ who gave_ me no way_ to han - dle things,_ who_

36

made me so bad. Ma - ma, the weep - ing,

Ma - ma, the an - gels. No sleep in Heav - en

or Beth - le - hem.

SLIPPING THROUGH MY FINGERS

WORDS & MUSIC BY BENNY ANDERSSON & BJÖRN ULVAEUS

1.School bag in hand,___ she leaves home in the ear - ly morn - ing
(Verse 2 see block lyric)

wav - ing good - bye with an ab - sent - mind - ed smile.

I watch her go___ with a surge of that

well known sad - ness,   and I have to sit____ down____ for a while.____

The feel - ing____ that I'm los - ing her____ for - ev - er

and with - out real - ly en - ter - ing her world.____

I'm glad when - ev - er I____ can share her laugh - ter,   that

39

Verse 2:

Sleep in our eyes, her and me at the breakfast table
Barely awake I let precious time go by.
Then when she's gone there's that odd melancholy feeling
And a sense of guilt I can't deny.
What happened to the wonderful adventures,
The places I had planned for us to go?
Well, some of it we did but most we didn't
And why, I just don't know.

Slipping through my fingers *etc.*

SO MUCH BETTER

WORDS & MUSIC BY LAURENCE O'KEEFE & NELL BENJAMIN

47

48

Much bet-ter! 'Cause I am so__ much bet-ter than be-fore!__

May-be she's what you pre-fer,__

but hey, last year I was her.__ May-be you will change your mind,__

50

add CHORUS:

Mom will fall on the floor.___ Hey, Mom! Look at my name___ in black and white!___ Your daugh-ter's do - in' some-thing right!___ And I feel so___ much bet - ter. I'll be there on Mon- - day, nine___ o - 'clock.___ Then we will see___

N.C.

53

55

SOMEWHERE THAT'S GREEN

WORDS BY HOWARD ASHMAN
MUSIC BY ALAN MENKEN

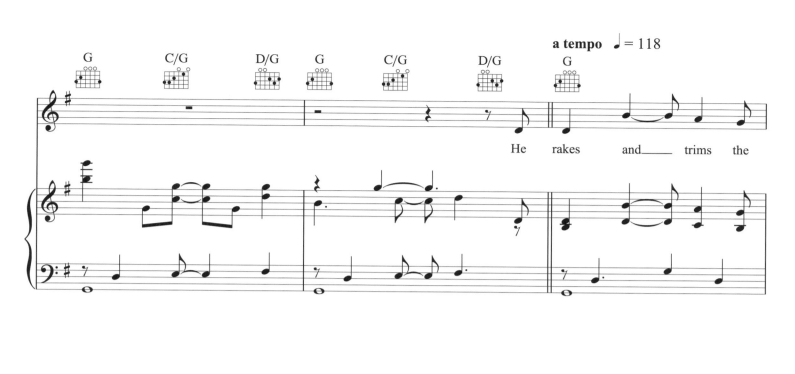

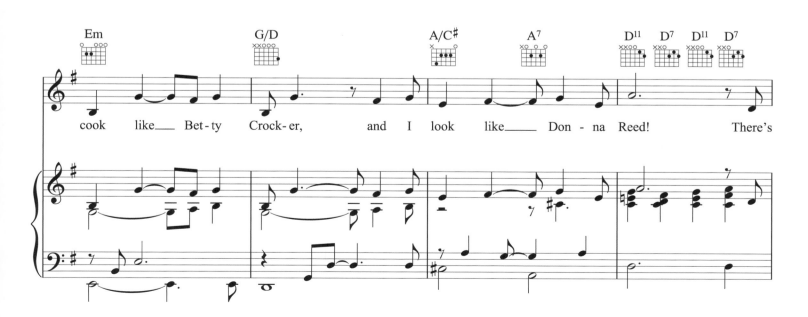

plas - tic___ on the furn - it - ure,___ to keep it neat and clean in the

Pine - Sol___ scent - ed air some - where that's green._____

___ Be - tween our fro - zen din - ner___ and our bed - time,___ nine fif -

- teen, we snug - gle watch - ing Lu - cy on our big e - nor - mous

WHEN YOU GOT IT, FLAUNT IT

WORDS & MUSIC BY MEL BROOKS

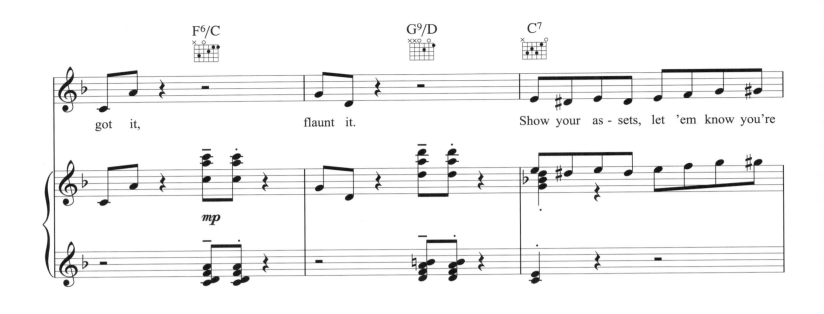

show it.   Put your hid-den treas-ures on dis-play.

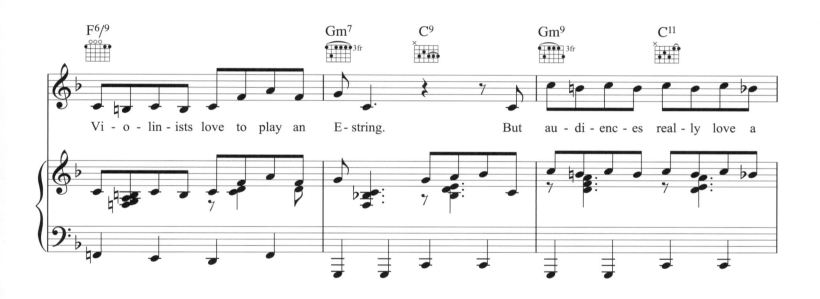

Vi-o-lin-ists love to play an E-string.   But au-di-enc-es real-ly love a

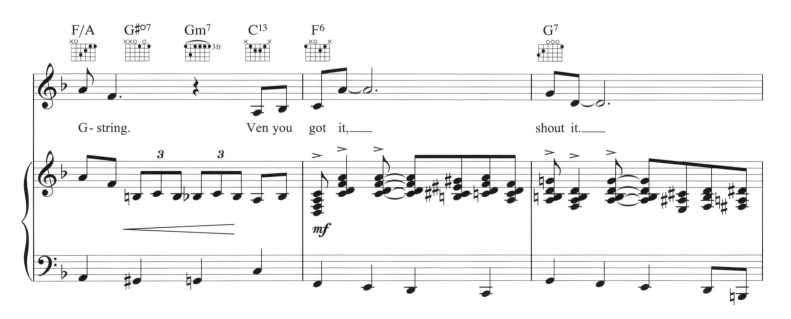

G-string.   Ven you got it,___   shout it.___

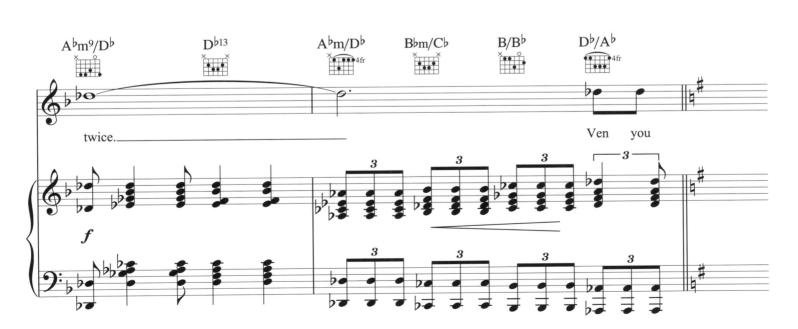

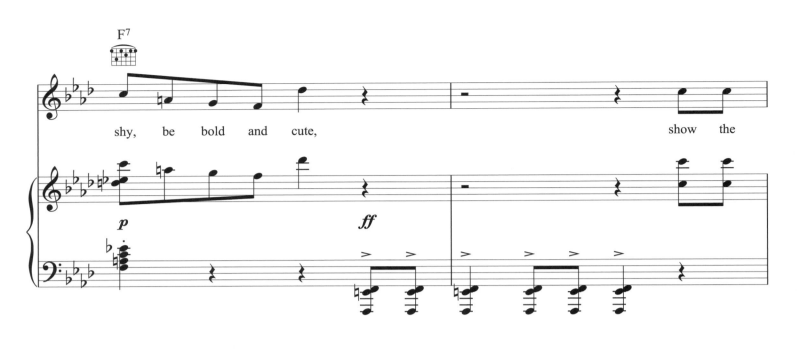

shy, be bold and cute, show the

boys that birth - day suit. Ven you

"Going home"

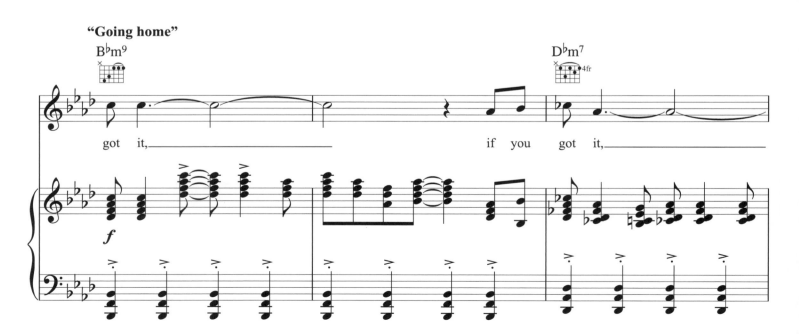

got it,_____ if you got it,_____

once you   got   it,   shout out hoo -

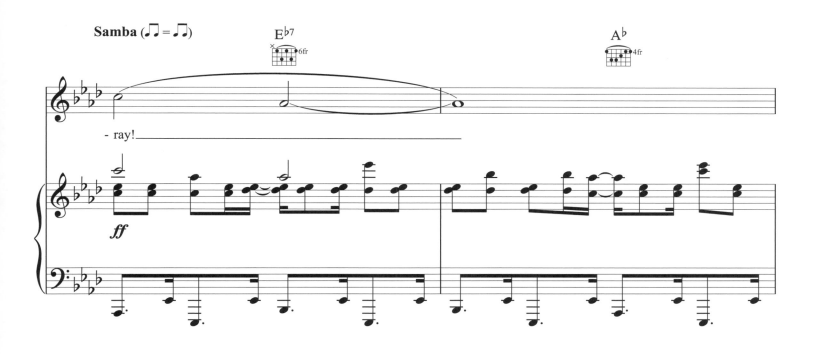

- ray!_____

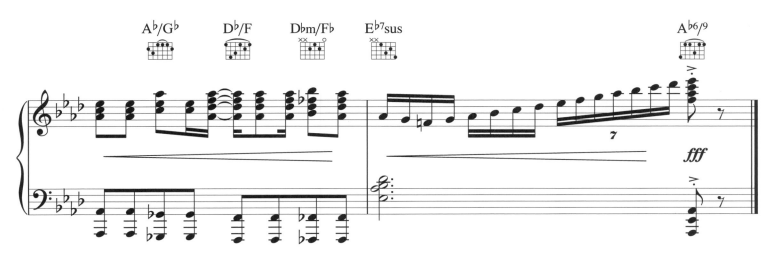

TAKE ME OR LEAVE ME

WORDS & MUSIC BY JONATHAN LARSON

don't lose your head,___ 'cause ev-'ry night, who's in your__ bed?_____

Who, who's_____ in your

bed?_____ Kiss, pook-ie! 3. It won't

or leave me.

D.S. al Coda Coda

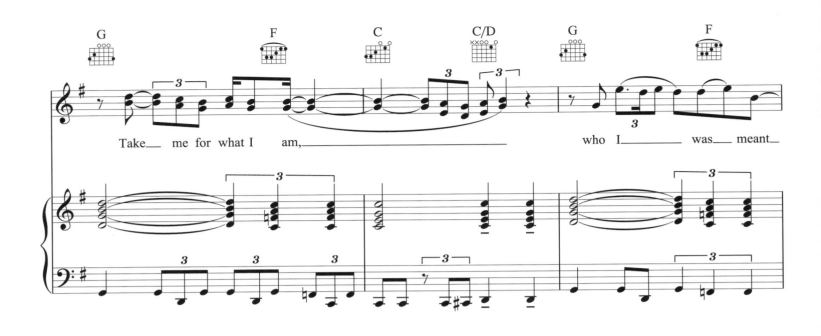

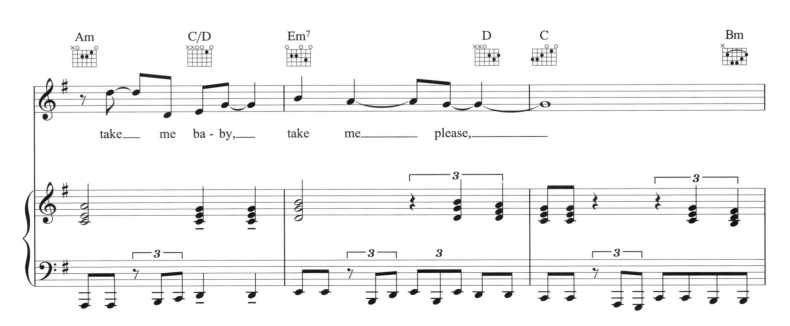

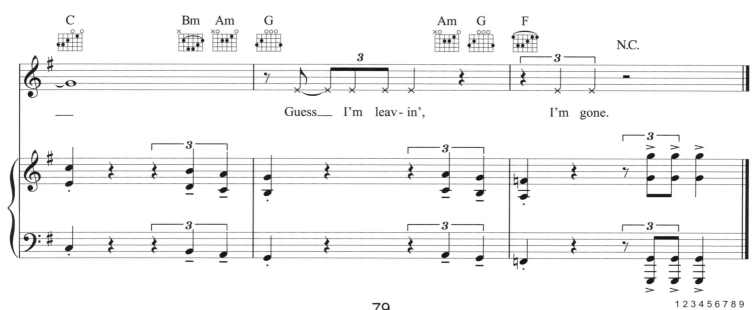

123456789

CD TRACK LISTING

AND I AM TELLING YOU I'M NOT GOING
DREAMGIRLS
CD TRACK 1
(EYEN/KRIEGER) UNIVERSAL MUSIC PUBLISHING LIMITED/UNIVERSAL/MCA MUSIC LIMITED

BE ITALIAN
NINE
CD TRACK 2
(YESTON) CHERRY LANE MUSIC LIMITED

DEFYING GRAVITY
WICKED
CD TRACK 3
(SCHWARTZ) GREYDOG MUSIC

GOOD MORNING BALTIMORE
HAIRSPRAY
CD TRACK 4
(SHAIMAN/WITTMAN) SONGS OF PEN UK

MAMA WHO BORE ME
SPRING AWAKENING
CD TRACK 5
(SATER/SHEIK) WARNER/CHAPPELL NORTH AMERICA LIMITED/
UNIVERSAL MUSIC PUBLISHING INTERNATIONAL MGB LIMITED /UNIVERSAL MUSIC PUBLISHING MGB LIMITED

SLIPPING THROUGH MY FINGERS
MAMMA MIA!
CD TRACK 6
(ANDERSSON/ULVAEUS) BOCU MUSIC LIMITED

SO MUCH BETTER
LEGALLY BLONDE
CD TRACK 7
(O'KEEFE/BENJAMIN) USEFUL YAK MUSIC/EMI MUSIC PUBLISHING LIMITED

SOMEWHERE THAT'S GREEN
LITTLE SHOP OF HORRORS
CD TRACK 8
(ASHMAN/MENKEN) WARNER/CHAPPELL MUSIC NORTH AMERICA LIMITED/
UNIVERSAL/MCA MUSIC LIMITED

WHEN YOU GOT IT, FLAUNT IT
THE PRODUCERS
CD TRACK 9
(BROOKS) HORNALL BROTHERS MUSIC LIMITED

TAKE ME OR LEAVE
RENT
CD TRACK 10
(LARSON) UNIVERSAL MUSIC PUBLISHING LIMITED/UNIVERSAL/MCA MUSIC LIMITED